The Space Race

'The Space Race'
An original concept by Jenny Jinks
© Jenny Jinks

Illustrated by Serena Lombardo

Published by MAVERICK ARTS PUBLISHING LTD
Studio 3A, City Business Centre, 6 Brighton Road,
Horsham, West Sussex, RH13 5BB
© Maverick Arts Publishing Limited August 2018
+44 (0)1403 256941

A CIP catalogue record for this book is available at the British Library.

ISBN 978-1-84886-364-4

www.maverickbooks.co.uk

Yellow

This book is rated as: Yellow Band (Guided Reading)
This story is decodable at Letters and Sounds Phase 3/4.

The Space Race

by **Jenny Jinks**

illustrated by **Serena Lombardo**

This is Zip.

He is from planet Zill.

This is Zog, from planet Zeek.

Zog and Zip took part in

a big race.

Zip had a big rocket.

Zog had a big ship.

"I will win," said Zip.

"My rocket is quick."

"No, I will win," said Zog.

"My ship is quicker."

"3...2...1...GO!"

They shot off.

"I can win this," said Zip.

"I will set my boosters to max!"

ZOOM!

But then... a booster fell off.

"I can win this!" said Zog.

"I will turn up my jets!"

ZOOM!

But then... a jet fell off.

"I can help you," said Zip.

"I can help you too," said Zog.

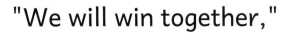

"We will win together,"

said Zip and Zog.

And they did!

Quiz

1. What planet is Zip from?
a) Mars
b) Earth
c) Zill

2. What are Zip and Zog in?
a) A race
b) A house
c) A party

3. What does Zip say when a booster falls off?
a) Oh no!
b) Hooray!
c) Hmmm

4. What sound does Zog's ship make?

a) Roar!

b) Beep!

c) Zoom!

5. Who wins the race?

a) Zip

b) Zip and Zog

c) Zog

Turn over for answers

Book Bands for Guided Reading

Pink

Red

Yellow

Blue

Green

Orange

Turquoise

Purple

Gold

White

The Institute of Education book banding system is a scale of colours that reflects the various levels of reading difficulty. The bands are assigned by taking into account the content, the language style, the layout and phonics.

Maverick Early Readers are a bright, attractive range of books covering the pink to purple bands. All of these books have been book banded for guided reading to the industry standard and edited by a leading educational consultant.

To view the whole Maverick Readers scheme, visit our website at
www.maverickearlyreaders.com

Or scan the QR code above to view our scheme instantly!

Quiz Answers: 1c, 2a, 3a, 4c, 5b